MIND GROWN

Note from the Author

This book is shaped by several things. Reading, listening, and watching others has provided a background for this book, as has my past. These stories have resonated with me for one reason or another.

This is just advice. It may not work for you, but there's a good chance it will. This is not medical advice; rather, this book contains entertaining stories and thoughts that I believe in.

Please read this book for enjoyment.

MIND GROWN

Tips, Tricks and Stories that can help grow your mindset into your most powerful tool

MATT ROMANO

Contents

For my sons, and my 12-year-old self.

Introduction

You've picked up this book and started to read, so thank you! I hope this isn't your last sentence and you keep going. I think you will find some value in what lies ahead.

The setup is simple: This book is a collection of short stories that are loosely based on experiences I've come across in life. Included are lessons I wish I had known earlier and wish someone had explained to me.

As kids, we have a lot of new information thrown at us. We are constantly learning, and we are forced to learn from and listen to teachers and adults every day. Math and science are important to learn, but there are other things we need to hear from others to guide us in the right direction. By the way, you will never stop learning—it's a fundamental part of life. Please don't shut yourself off from learning by thinking you know almost everything. You don't. Not even close. As you grow, make it your mission to never stop growing. It's a fascinating thing to realize you will never know it all. Those who think they do won't have a fulfilling, purposeful life.

If you think about it, you make thousands of choices each day. You made a choice to pick up this book and a choice to keep reading after the first sentence. Soon, you'll be making a choice to eat or avoid the cupcake that's sitting on your counter. Next choice: glass of milk with it? Sit on the couch? Shoot some hoops? Do your homework? Bother your brother while he's trying to do his homework? Get it? You make choices all the time.

For me, having all these choices can be hard, and it can be nice to have a little help, something to look back at, or someone like me who has faced the choice before and can provide some guidance.

Stories are a great way to understand a lesson. That's why I picked this way. It's your "choice" if you want to read this once and never again, read only the chapters that sound interesting, or use this book as a reference when you find yourself in some of these situations.

I have one favor to ask you before you start and while you read: Keep an open mind. While you're reading, do not form any opinions or make any assumptions. Take the stories for what they are—just stories—and enjoy them. Just know that *everyone* is going through something…just like you.

Ok, enough, let's go!

Chapter 1

The Voice

We were down one point, and I had the ball at the free throw line. One shot. There was no time on the clock, and it was just me, alone with the ball and the hoop. I'd been here before—only it was in my driveway and my friend Tim was usually shaking the hoop. There were two outcomes that could happen, and my mind was racing just about as fast as my mom had driven to get me to the game on time.

I could smell the butter from the popcorn my sister was eating in the stands and realized how quiet the gymnasium was. All eyes were on me. My teammates were all counting on me.

Suddenly, a voice from the distance yelled, "You'll never make this shot."

As I stood there, sweat dripping off my forehead, I couldn't believe that someone would actually say that to me. It rattled me. It froze me. It made me question all the free throws I've made in my life. It's all I could think about and all I could hear.

My arms felt like Jell-O, and I put up the shot. CLANK. Front rim, not even close. We lost. My teammates were disappointed but gave me high-fives anyway. I'm not sure what they said to me, because all I could think about was that voice that shouted at me. Seriously, who the heck was that and why didn't my dad go over and punch him like he deserved?

Our coach brought us into the locker room and gave us an inspiring speech—I think. I'm not sure because I was just listening to the replay of that voice.

In the car ride home, I asked my mom and dad how someone could be so mean with their words and who that person had been. Mom claimed she didn't hear it, but I think she just wanted to change the subject so it wouldn't eat at me, and I would just forget about it.

I got the same reaction from my friends the next day. It was so weird.

I began to think about how I had heard a voice three weeks ago that sounded eerily similar, right before I had to present in front of my geography class. I was about to have my name called as I sat there in a panic, hoping Mr. Jones had somehow forgotten it was my turn to go.

I remember thinking it was Adam, who always was shouting out in class. He said, "You'll never get an A. Hope you don't forget what you are going to say. That would be embarrassing."

But the voices sounded similar—maybe Adam was at the game?

Wait a second… I had heard that voice when I went to a Christmas party and was super nervous to see my cousins, who were so much cooler than me. That voice said to me, "You are not as cool as your cousins. They probably think you are such a dork. Have fun… hope they don't laugh at you."

But you know what? I had been alone in my room when that voice said that to me. Seriously, no one was home at the time.

I know I don't talk to myself, but I do remember my dad telling me about the voice that everyone has inside of them that produces certain thoughts. He likes to "preach" about certain things, and I usually just nod and wink but barely listen. (Sorry, Dad!)

Could the voice that shouted at the basketball game, the one that told me I'd never get an A, and told me my cousins think I'm a dork really be me?

It sounds crazy, but if they all sound similar maybe it just could be. Maybe that's why no one else can hear it.

I decided to ask my Uncle Tony, the nicest, most soft-spoken uncle you could have. He didn't speak a lot, but when he did, what he said always froze me in time and made me think. He had a lot of memories and experiences to share, and I always loved listening to him.

One day I caught him while he was drinking coffee, reading the newspaper, and eating milk crackers. (Yuck!) I asked him about the voice I kept hearing and asked if he knew where it could be coming from.

He put down the paper and looked at me, smiling.

"That's your inner voice," he said. "It's an important voice in your life that will always be with you no matter what." He went on, "When I was growing up, I had a real battle with my inner voice and realized that it was always kind of mean to me. I learned that I had to train my voice to be a friend and someone I could always count on.

"One of the reasons I succeeded in basketball as a teacher and a father is because my inner voice was there to guide me and was not a voice of destruction. I made the voice into someone who built me up when times were tough instead of trying to knock me down.

"If you want to fix this, here's what you need to do. Ask yourself this question: Would you want to be friends with the voice that is inside your brain? If the answer is no, YOU can change it. Every time you hear a negative thought, spin it to the positive. Think the opposite. Instead of, 'What if this goes wrong?' think, 'What if this goes right?'

"Everyone around you, including me, is rooting for you. There is absolutely no reason you shouldn't be rooting for yourself.

"Next time you're on the free throw line, DON'T THINK, 'This is tough. I might miss this.' Instead, THINK, 'I have practiced this. I can do this.'"

I sat there in silence as it started to make sense.

He said one final thing. "Do me one favor: The next time you have a negative thought or a hear a negative voice, don't listen to it. Flip it and tell yourself the opposite. Force yourself to believe in yourself and in your abilities. I promise, soon enough, you'll begin to see the difference and re-train that voice. After all, that voice is yours, and no one but YOU controls it."

Chapter 2

There Is Someone
in Your Corner

The phrase, "Have someone in your corner," is a cliché that is often used, but you may not know its backstory.

It comes from the sport of boxing. A fighter must go to the middle of the boxing ring and fight their opponent. It's one-on-one—you vs. them. A boxing match has timed rounds, and when the time is over, each boxer goes back to their "corner" of the ring.

Every boxer has a coach, a doctor, and other team members in their corner. It's their support system to help them in their boxing match journey.

Every boxer needs this crew and so does every kid.

Some of us have big corners and big families and lots of supportive friends. Some of us don't. It's ok if you don't, but just know there is always someone in your corner. Even if it seems like you have no one to talk to or no one to go to after that round is over, you just need to look harder.

————————————————————

It was time to find a job. My parents had given me everything I needed, but I was reaching the age where I could and should be earning money on my own. I went to college for a year, and I liked it but didn't do well, so I had to come home and start over.

My dad pushed me to get a job, and I made a lot of excuses as to why I didn't get one.

One of my problems was that I became a "nervous Nelly." I became anxious when it was time to do just about anything that didn't involve hanging out with my friends or sleeping. It was a tough time in my life, but something I and a lot of other kids just had to get through.

Anyway, I got a job interview at a Kohl's department store. I was nervous and my inner voice was telling me all the wrong things. The job was manual labor, unloading trucks of product and putting it out so other employees could stock it.

I went to the interview and found myself in the back with about 15 people also there for an interview.

It was going to be a group interview with all the potential employees in a room and we all would answer questions together.

Well, I wasn't cool with this. I hated talking in front of people, let alone 15 people. Speaking in front of a group wasn't my thing. (It's not many peoples' thing.)

I started to sweat and freak out. I thought quickly about how I could get out of there. I'd tell my dad I just didn't get the job, I guess.

I started to slowly walk away and down the aisle to the front of the store. I was almost gone. *Phew, that would have stunk*, I thought. *I would probably have said something stupid or stuttered or made a fool of myself.* (THESE ARE ALL THE WRONG THOUGHTS TO HAVE.)

As I walked away, I heard a voice from the back that said, "Excuse me, sir. The interview is about to start."

It was an older woman who must have been about 70. She reminded me of my grandma when I looked back at her.

"Who, me?" I asked.

"Yes, the interview is starting now. Hurry back," she said.

I don't know who this lady was or why she said this to me. I wonder if she could feel the lostness of where I was in life. Or maybe she was just very kind and didn't want me to miss out.

Whatever it was, I didn't have an excuse, so I just walked back and into that interview room.

I thanked her, but I was super nervous again.

We all filed into a room, and I was asked a question. Guess what? I answered the question, and everyone seemed to like my answer. I had built it up so much in my mind that I thought it would feel like I was being questioned by the police about a crime.

I just didn't have self-confidence, but I knew I was smart and was able to do tough things if I just pushed myself.

On the way out, I couldn't find the older woman, as I wanted to thank her. She single-handedly had helped me get that job and gain some much-needed self-confidence.

In fact, I never saw her again, and to this day, I can't tell you what she looked like.

But I know one thing: she was in my corner.

Sometimes you will find the people who are in your corner are the ones you least expect.

It could be a total stranger like a little old lady.

It could be that mean kid in your science class who really isn't that mean. You might find out he's rooting for you to make the soccer team and gives you a tip on how to improve.

It could be your grandma who comes over and tells you, "I believe in you," every day.

Hold onto these people. Put them in your corner and try to keep them there. Everyone needs them.

Even if you think you have no one in your corner, I promise you, someone is there. You may need to look just a little bit harder, and they might just come out when you least expect it, like at a job interview.

By the way, I was amazing at that job. I unloaded boxes like a champ! I owe you one, little old lady.

Chapter 3

Face Your Adversity

When you are faced with a tough decision or obstacle, people will tell you that you won't feel good if you run from it as fast as you can. But it *will* feel good. You will feel a rush from not having to make that decision, and you will be happy about not having to deal with it.

Remember the story I told about getting a job at Kohl's? I was so nervous for the group interview that I started to walk away. I've done that in my life before, and I knew how good I would feel when I got into my car and drove away. I could see myself driving out of the parking lot and getting on the road. Every step I took toward the front of the store and the exit became faster, and I got excited. It was almost like the feeling when you wake up on Christmas morning. You float down the steps to see if there are presents.

That's the feeling I had. Santa had brought me a big box of "get the heck out of here!"

Once I got in my car, no one would be able to stop me, and my feelings of nervousness would be gone. I became used to that feeling and knew where to find it. It was kind of like a down and up type of feeling. I would have some sort of problem, or something would be in my way, and I'd find a way around it by not having to deal with it. Once I knew I didn't have to deal with it, I'd feel really good.

BUT...what the Kohl's experience showed me is there is an even better feeling, one that requires you to trust yourself. The feeling of facing your problem head-on and succeeding is so much better than running away. Trust me on this.

Even if you don't succeed after taking on this big challenge, well, it's not as bad as you think it will be. You'll even learn about the mistakes you made or what went wrong.

As you grow older, you will hear this: "Failure is not the opposite of success; it's part of success." Seems like a joke, right? It's not. No one who has made a successful decision has done so without first encountering some sort of failure.

In fact, I've found that the greatest players in sports have failed many times. They just kept getting back up because they believed in themselves and their abilities.

For example, Michael Jordan, arguably the greatest basketball player ever, got cut from his high school basketball team. Tom Brady, arguably the greatest quarterback of all time, had 198 players taken before him in the NFL draft.

When I played soccer as a kid, I had an amazing coach who taught me a lot about the game. When I first started to play, he would always say, "At the end of the game, when the score is tied, you need to WANT to have the ball at your feet."

Well, I always thought the opposite. I kind of hoped I wasn't in the game at the end, and that no one would pass me the ball.

After a game, I'd feel a sense of excitement that I didn't mess anything up. I didn't have an opportunity to screw anything up with the game on the line. It felt good...really good.

But I kept thinking about what he said, and one day I decided to *listen* rather than just hear him.

We were down, 1-0 with a couple minutes left at a tournament in Rhode Island. I became invigorated with a sense of energy. I played sweeper, a position on defense that controlled the back line. It was rare to get scoring opportunities from back there, but this sense of energy was a new feeling for me, and I decided to just go for it. I saw the ball at the feet of one of the best playmakers on our team. I knew if I made a run up top, he'd feel the energy and see me moving, so I broke for it.

He put a ball through, right past their last defender. It was perfect, *so* perfect! I ran onto it, and then it was just the goalie and me. I had to make maybe ten dribbles to get there, but I just had to put it past him.

Guess what happened next?

I freaking failed. I got two cramps in both of my calves, at the same time! I'm not even sure how that can happen, but it happened to me. We had played three games that day and my muscles were exhausted.

I fell to the ground—probably on my face— and the goalie came out to clear the ball.

The whistle blew for an injury timeout. I was in pain, but the pain was nothing compared to the embarrassment I felt.

I had gone for it which was against my thinking. I was so dumb. Why did I do that? I felt like a failure. Never again.

The game had ended, and I was on the sideline, trying not to make eye contact with anyone. Shame was on my face, big time.

Tony, our amazing playmaker came up to me and said, "Dude, that was a nasty run. It sucks how it ended, but you put yourself in a great position for me to pass you that ball. I didn't even know you were that fast, man."

Our coach then came up to me. I was thinking he would say something to make me feel better or maybe he would yell at me for getting out of position. He said neither.

"Matt, that was a great run. You were so close to tying this game. You need to keep doing this, and maybe we need to get you up the field more with that speed."

I was in shock. Neither of them had said anything about how I blew it. Everyone just complimented me.

Coach asked, "How did you know to make that run?"

"I just had a hunch," I said. "I guess just an instinct."

"You need to keep following that instinct," he said.

I started to move up the field and became more of a playmaker. When it was the end of the game, I needed the ball at my feet. I became aggressive and a better teammate.

It was all because of failure. I failed badly that day, but there was a lesson that helped me, and it still helps me to this day.

Even though I failed, was it really that bad?

The instinct, the hunch that I was talking about? Everyone has it. You may already take things head-on no matter what. But maybe you don't.

If you don't, just try it. It's like pizza: once you try it, you will like it.

The feeling of taking on a huge boulder in your way far outweighs running away from it. Running away may feel good, but it's a short-term feeling.

Find your instinct, find your hunch, and, just as coach said, "You need to keep following that instinct."

Chapter 4

Anxiety Lives in the Future

Ever since I can remember, I have never stopped thinking. I am constantly thinking, almost to the point that sometimes I can't focus on what is happening in the moment. Maybe that's how you are and maybe it isn't.

When I am in a car with someone and there is silence for a while, I like to ask that person, "What were you thinking?"

When that person says "Nothing," I am always so jealous. It is a skill to have a quiet and relaxed mind and to almost shut off your brain.

For me, it is something I must focus on and work to control.

I like to imagine my brain has arms and legs and that it's constantly running a marathon. My brain is even wearing a head band and just running and running.

While it's good to have a brain that exercises and is used, it also needs some time to chill. For me, I really need to work on that. I try to picture that same brain sitting on the couch just eating potato chips. I want and need that chilled-out brain at times! Sometimes it works, and sometimes it doesn't.

I also like to imagine swiping out my thoughts, just like when you close apps on an iPhone. I swipe every thought that comes to me until I finally get rid of them all. Sometimes it takes quite a while, and sometimes I even give up.

The real problem I've run into is that my thoughts can keep going and start to travel way too far into the future. They create their own story, and usually it is nothing like how the future will play out.

What I've found is that nervousness and anxiety live in the future. When your mind goes there, those bullies will find you.

When you think too far ahead, you make yourself nervous for absolutely no reason.

I was standing in front of the mirror in my room. My door was locked shut while I stood there, staring myself in the eyes.

My thoughts were going a million miles a minute, and I was struck with a panic I had never felt before.

I tried to breathe, but even that seemed hard at the moment.

I was always nervous when I had to present in front of the class, but this time it was different. I was a sophomore in high school, and I had a 25-minute presentation to do in English class.

I thought about keeping my door locked and climbing under the covers for the day. If I kept the door locked, maybe my parents would forget about me. Or if I refused to come out, they might have to call the fire department to come knock down my door. That would surely take longer than two hours. By the time I got out, my English class would be over!

Considering my parents had a key to the door, this seemed unlikely.

I had built up this moment in my head since the day my teacher announced it three months prior. There would be times I was hanging out with my friends or playing basketball, and I'd be having a great time. Then suddenly I would remember, and a wave of panic would come over my body. Later, I'd learn this was the worst thing I could do.

I had thought about the presentation so much in the last few days that I hadn't been eating like normal due to the unnecessary nervousness I had.

I ran out of excuses and options. I looked at myself, took a deep breath, and headed out the door to the bus. I didn't talk to anyone on the bus. A couple kids tried to talk to me, but I scowled at them and just stared down at my feet.

I talked to no one that day and can't tell you what anyone said to me. All I could think about was stuttering or spitting on myself or forgetting everything in my presentation. I was prepared and I had practiced, but I still had no confidence that I would be ok.

Well, the time came, and my teacher called on me to come to the front of the class.

I walked up slowly, felt like I was going to puke and then…

I did totally fine.

I started out nervous and was speaking softly, but it went pretty darn good! I said what I needed to say because I had practiced. Just like that, it was over, I felt great and got a B+.

My classmates applauded, and all I could think about was, "Why the heck did I just waste three months worrying about nothing?"

Maybe the day of the presentation I should have been nervous because that's a natural feeling, but I had made up a huge story about how I was going to stutter and forget how to speak like a human.

What a waste! I was so annoyed.

Ever since that day, I try to focus on the moment and what I can control about the things that are happening in front of me.

I tell myself, "Be where your feet are."

It's waste of time to focus on the future and to think about things that are days, weeks, or months away, because you will miss what's going on right in front of you. More than likely, whatever is coming up ahead will take care of itself if you have self-confidence and prepare for the journey.

The preparation I did for this specific journey was to study my subject and practice my speech. What I didn't and shouldn't have done was to worry and make up a story about what might happen three months in the future.

Being anxious is when you feel fear or uneasiness. It's not a good feeling, but it's something you can fix. It still gets me sometimes, but one thing that helps is to focus on what's going on right now, in this moment.

Mind Grown

Be where your feet are and don't lose sight of what's in front of your face, because bad things can happen when you think too far ahead.

Chapter 5

Dismiss the Outside Noise

Remember when we talked about that inner voice back in Chapter 1? Well, you need to know how to use that voice, but you also need to realize that this voice is the only one that really matters.

Support from your family and friends is important, and their voices will be inspiration, but the only voice that matters is the one that drives you… your own.

People can't help but judge others and say their opinions out loud. Any decision you make will have more people questioning you than supporting you. (When you find the people who support you, make sure to hold onto them because they are hard to find!)

Every decision I have made has come with someone saying, "You can't do that," or "That is not a good choice. You'll never succeed."

It is not easy to tune them out, but it is a MUST if you want to live your own life and follow your own path.

If you want to take it a step further, flip that voice and turn it into fuel to drive you to your goal or destination.

═══════════════════════

I had been playing the guitar for about a year. I played mostly in my room, by myself. It was a hobby I really enjoyed, and I found I was pretty good at it. I had musical talent from an early age. Once I picked up a guitar, I just taught myself.

I had started getting better and showing friends my new skill. I also started to sing a little and found out, based on others' reactions, that I was pretty good at that too.

It was my senior year of high school, and there was a talent show coming up. My friend Sam kept telling me that I had to play a song. He would say, "It's a talent show, and you've got talent. You need to show it off. But only you can make the decision."

That showed me I had someone in my corner who believed in me.

It also showed me that the only voice that *mattered* was my own. No one else could make this decision for me, and I couldn't rely on the advice of someone who wasn't with me every single hour of every single day.

I was shy and didn't like attention, but I told him I would think about it.

At this point in my life, I relied on other people's opinions to guide me. I learned later that I didn't need their opinions because a lot of times they just complicated my own thoughts.

I asked other friends what they thought, and one of my friends (I won't name them!) offered his opinion.

He said, "Do you know how hard it is to play in front of a crowd? I'm not sure you are even that good. That will be super hard. Keep practicing."

After hearing this, I realized there weren't just two answers. A third one started to appear.

1. I could listen to that advice and not play in the talent show,
2. I could dismiss what they were saying, OR
3. I could take that answer as fuel to push me to take the challenge.

Being competitive my whole life, when I heard this, something snapped inside me and woke me up.

Many people would listen to this advice and run away from something challenging but not me, not this time.

I've done that too much in my life.

I realized this response was the confirmation I needed to go for a new challenge. Who cares if it is hard? Why would I want to stay on Easy Street? Easy is boring. Easy doesn't get you to where you want to go.

That was the assurance I needed to take the leap. I knew I wanted to be different, and I knew I wanted to be challenged.

I played in the talent show, and it was one of the best decisions that I could have made. It turned out to be a stepping stone in the right direction. Even if it had been a stepping stone in the wrong direction, or if I had failed, it still would have shown me a lesson: You can always step on another stone.

Right before the show, when I told Sam I would do it, he was excited, but then he asked me, "Is it what YOU want?"

He made a good point. He didn't want me to play the show just because *he* thought it was a good idea. He wanted me to do it only if *I* thought it was a good idea.

The next time you're faced with a tough decision, you can ask for advice, but don't make a decision based on someone else's feelings or someone else's opinion. Make sure you listen to your *own* advice and your *own* voice because when it all comes down to it, that's the ONLY one that matters.

Chapter 6

Don't Delay,
But It's OK if You Delay

What a title, huh? It makes no sense, but I've found that some things in life don't make any sense at all. It's just the way it is, and this is one of them.

When you're facing a decision or make some sort of move, it is best to not delay. But If for some reason it does get delayed, don't give up on it.

———————

I was a senior in high school, and we were coming off a cold winter. I played basketball in the winter and loved to play all sports. I had a great season that year, partly because in the summer between my junior and senior year of high school, I grew about four inches.

I became a much better athlete and found myself faster, stronger, and taller than I had been just a couple months before.

My friend ran track for the school and for four years had been telling me to try out for the track team. I was always fast but never had the confidence or drive to try it.

As he talked about it again, I felt different about it. Now that I was bigger and faster than I used to be, I thought I might be good at it.

He talked me into it. I tried out for the team and quickly started to run the 100 meters, 200 meters, and 110-meter hurdles.

It took me a while to learn the basics: how to start, how to jump hurdles without missing a stride, and how and when to push myself.

I was pretty good at it. I became a member of the 4 x 100 team, a relay made up of four teammates who ran around the track for 100 meters each, then passed a baton to the next person.

There were three experienced guys on the team who helped me, and I became the fourth person who made us even faster.

It was the end of the year at one of our biggest track meets. We all got to the start, and everything clicked. I ran my fastest time, and we set a school record that day. We still hold that record.

I remember the next day thinking, *What if I had started running track four years ago? I would be so much faster. I'd have much better technique. Maybe I'd be running track in college.*

I saw my friend Mike and said, "Why didn't you work harder to try to convince me?"

He looked at me and said, "At least I was able to convince you this year. Otherwise, you'd never have this experience."

He was right. Instead of thinking about the "what if," I needed to be thankful that I had finally decided to run.

Would I have been better with more practice and experience? Yes.

Would I have had the experience if I never said yes? Nope.

It's better if you don't delay a decision, but it's probably not too late. Don't let adults tell you that it's too late because it's just not true. All that matters is what you want.

Sometimes the time isn't right. Sometimes you need an added confidence boost to help you with that decision.

There are many times in my life that I started something later than I should have. I graduated college at age 29! But I got it done because I wanted to.

It may have been a different path than some, but we still all met at the same finish line.

Everyone has a different story and a different way of doing things. There isn't one answer and there isn't one decision you will be tied to. If you think you made the wrong one, fix it.

When you're faced with a decision, make it the best as possible. If you make the right one, you'll be ahead of the game, but if you make the wrong one, just know that it's not too late to fix it.

Chapter 7

Make Kindness #1

Everyone is going through something. EVERYONE. You will never know most of it.

When you cross paths with someone, the easiest thing to do is judge them, find their weakness, or complain about them.

It's something I struggle with daily.

As in most of the stories and lessons I've shared, this is about doing the thing that most people don't. Your true potential lies in doing the uncommon thing. It's easy to go with the crowd, but it takes a lot of courage to do the opposite, if you believe in it.

Being uncommon is a common theme for me. Remembering this helps me on my journey.

Being kind and generous to others is one of those uncommon things. Plus, I promise, it will make you feel great when someone looks up and meets your kindness with a smile.

―――――――――――――――――――――――

I was about 12. I had just gotten home from school, and I stormed through the door. No one was home, or so I thought.

I ran to my room and collapsed on my bed. Earlier in the day, the middle school basketball team was announced on a piece of paper on the locker room wall. I was excited to see who would be on my team.

As I looked at the paper, I didn't see my name. I re-read all the names. Then I re-read it again.

My name was nowhere to be found. There was no way I had been cut from the team. I had a good tryout, and I was good at hooping.

As I read the names for the 7th time, I realized it. I had been cut. There was no middle school basketball team for me.

I was angry and then pretty darn sad. I couldn't stop my eyes from tearing up.

I had never thought about not being on the team.

Fast forward to when I got home from school. I was on my bed, staring at the ceiling, overwhelmed with the embarrassment of being cut.

Also, earlier that same day, I had received a D on an English paper, just to make things that much worse.

As I was lying there, I heard some footsteps coming into the room. I thought it might be my friend Tim who would always sneak into my house unannounced.

But it wasn't him. It was my Aunt Patti.

Patti had moved in with us after my grandmother passed away. She had lived with my grandma her whole life.

Patti had Down syndrome, which is associated with intellectual disability, among other things. Patti could not process complex ideas or thoughts. She would never be able to live alone and had to be taken care of, due to some physical and growth disabilities.

One thing this disease did not take away from her was her ability to be kind. She always saw the good in everything, no matter how bad it could have been.

She came into my room that day, saw that I was sad, and just sat on my bed and rubbed my back.

She didn't ask me what had happened. She didn't want to hear about what was wrong. She simply just wanted to be there for someone who was going through a hard time.

This is just one of many stories about her kindness. Kindness was her greatest asset. No matter what happened in my day, she was always there with a kind heart, no matter what.

I think about what made her great. Part of it was that she was just uncomplicated. When you were with her, you realized the stupid, day-to-day problems you were dealing with were no match for Down syndrome and what she had to deal with every single day of her life since birth.

Many times, I came home in a bad mood, nervous or anxious about something, and I would just see her, and it would all disappear. I would think about how my problem was nothing compared to her physical and mental issues. And yet, she was the kindest soul you could ever know.

If you're asking, "What is kindness?" the simple definition is being friendly, generous, and considerate. It's not anything specific; rather, it's an emotion, and it's a very simple thing to do.

Sometimes you don't need to understand what others are going through, but you do have to understand that everyone is going through something.

When you are young, you might think that everything in the world is great. Everyone is happy, and no one deals with any problems. Then you grow older and find out this is the farthest thing from the truth.

The sooner you realize this, the better you will be. The kinder you are to every single person, the better you will feel, and the better they will feel.

The next time you want to judge someone or talk badly about something, before you do, tell yourself, everyone is going through something. Then ask yourself, what would Patti do?

Chapter 8

Everyone Struggles

One of my favorite quotes is by Johann Wolfgang von Goethe: "Enjoy when you can and endure when you must."

I think about multiple things when I read this:

1. Enjoy the good times when you have them because they may not last forever.
2. When you are in bad times, if you endure (follow through—patiently get through it) the correct way, the good times will return.
3. Everyone struggles.

The third item is what I want to focus on here. I'll say it again, everyone struggles. Every. Single. Person.

When I was a kid, I didn't realize this. In this new age of social media, it's tough not to think that every single person in the world is having a great time in life. I won't get started on social media, but it's definitely not a healthy place to shape our worldviews. It's not even close to reality.

———————————————————

I'm not sure which year it was, but I was a teenager. The time is blurry to me. I think it's funny how my memory is foggy about this period of my life, but maybe it's foggy for a reason. If we're being honest, there was a stretch where my family was dealing with a bunch of bad news, all in a row.

We were losing key parts of our extended family at times that just didn't make sense.

I won't go into detail because it's hard to remember, but the details don't matter to the story.

I grew up in a large, close-knit family. I would go to my grandparent's house every Sunday for dinner, and these are cherished memories. I remember feeling secure, without any problems or nervousness. Family can do that for you. When you're all together, a lot of your insecurities feel far away and out of memory.

As the family started to grow older, we lost some of them to death at early ages. A couple of these deaths really stung. Death is a hard thing to deal with when you're a kid. It's a tough thing to deal with no matter how old you are.

You never think about it until you have to deal with it. And then, BOOM, it hits you.

I'm not trying to scare you, but I think death is a good thing to talk about before you must deal with it. It will happen at some point in your life. You just don't know when.

Over the course of about two years, our family suffered maybe five or six deaths. A cousin, an uncle, grandmas, aunts. Sprinkle in the struggles of trying to grow up, and it wasn't a great recipe.

At first I thought, *Why us?* Every time it happened, I questioned why the heck it was happening to me. It was actually kind of a selfish thought. After all, it wasn't just happening to me, it was happening to everyone around me as well. But looking back, I was pretty closed-minded.

I would think about how my future would be affected, and all I could come up with was negative. "I will never get to talk sports again with this person." "I will never get to tell them I love them ever again." "I will never get to have them pick me up from school ever again."

The word "never" seems to be used a lot here.

I also thought these times and feelings of grief would never end.

You can't think that, because even though it's hard not to in that moment, the tough times won't last forever. It takes even longer to get out of these moments if you don't focus on the positive around you. Even if it seems there is no positive, you just have to dig deeper to find it. It's there.

As I think about it now, what if I had just worded these thoughts a little differently?

"When I talked sports with them, those were some of the best moments in my life, and I'll always remember them." "I'm really glad I was able to tell them I loved them hundreds of times." "Remember those times they picked me up from school? It won't happen again, but at least it did happen, and I will cherish those times forever."

You might be thinking it's easier to say it than to do it. This is 100% true. I need to force myself to do this when times are tough, and I can't always do it.

It's ok to think about the negatives in the situation, and you can think about them because that's the natural first instinct for most people. But then take all those thoughts and spin them in a more positive way.

No matter what's happening at this point in your life, the only constant is change. Get through it with the best possible attitude and enjoy the good times while they're happening.

If you're going through something great and feeling good, know that it won't last forever. There are obstacles that will come in your way.

If you're going through something hard and tough, know that it won't last forever. It will be much easier to get through it if you think about the positives that are happening instead of focusing on the negative, even when there is a lot of negative.

Another one of my favorite quotes is by Robert Schuller: "Tough times don't last, tough people do." It's a well-known quote for a reason, because it's true. If you follow through and stick out your tough times with a good attitude, they won't last.

It's easy to give up. That's what so many people do when times are tough. It's not easy to always keep your head up.

But when you think about the things you are grateful for, that will move your focus from the bad things and help you center on the good that is going on in your life. Chances are, you have a lot of good and positive things happening around you.

Remember, this moment is not your life, it's just a moment *in* your life. The good moments and the bad moments won't last forever. Enjoy the good and make the best of the bad, because in the end, no matter when that is, it will just be a small snapshot of who you are.

Chapter 9

Process Over Outcome

It's about the journey, not the end.

Every January 1st, many people throughout the world write down their goals for the upcoming year. I try to do this every year. Goals are great to have, but I find that even if I don't hit the goal at the end of the year, if I am able to get close to it, I am still happy with myself.

Too many people have the wrong idea about goals when they start the new year. Most of them are quantifiable, meaning they can be measured or have a number attached.

For example:

"I want to run 5 miles without stopping."

"I want to score 12 goals this year during hockey season."

"I want to read 10 books this year."

While these types of goals provide a target, if you have a goal of reading 12 books in a year and you read 11, does that mean you missed your goal, and it was a failure? Of course not.

The goals I now make are "goal verbs." What do I mean by that? The definition of a *verb* is a word that conveys an action, occurrence, or state of being. If our goals can be actions, we are more likely to succeed in those goals.

Don't get me wrong, there are times when you'll want or need to put numbers next to goals. You should still do this, but if you come up short, don't tell yourself you didn't make it if you succeeded in the *action* of moving yourself toward that goal.

For example:

"I want to score 12 goals this year during hockey season."

You scored 9 and had 14 assists, played in every game, and were a leader for your team. You didn't hit the quantity goal, but you still had your best year on the ice.

This is where the journey matters more than the ending. The verb or action matters more than the result.

I was trapped in the car for five hours. I was meeting my aunt halfway between my house and Maine. My grandmother was driving, and we were listening to some old, bad music. I wasn't listening to the music. I was listening to my thoughts, filled with excitement and nervousness.

I was going to soccer camp in Maine. It wasn't just any soccer camp. It was a soccer camp run by the head coach of the Notre Dame soccer team. It was going to be something new, something exciting, and something not every kid my age would get to experience.

The air conditioning wasn't working, and I was sweating out of my eyeballs. I was thinking hard about what the camp would be like, and I made a goal right there in the car.

I promised myself I would work as hard as possible, and ultimately, I'd come back to high school and make the varsity team as a sophomore.

We finally arrived in Maine, and I showed up for my first day at camp. I was in awe of some of the college players who were my coaches. From the first minute, I excelled in every part of the camp.

I was the best all-around player on my team and earned the MVP award for my division and age group.

After five days, I couldn't have had more confidence. I became the exact player I wanted and knew I could be. I was in great shape and was ready for high school captains' practices and ultimately try outs.

It was the week before school and the first day of three tryouts. I laced up my cleats and worked my butt off.

Individual drills, team drills, scrimmages, and conditioning. I left it all out there. I never gave up. I really wanted a spot on the varsity team and knew hard work was the way to get it.

I was even more confident now, just waiting for the announcement of the rosters. There was no doubt I'd be getting that varsity uniform. I just hoped I'd get my sacred number 2!

The day of the announcement came, and you guessed it—just like the middle school basketball team—it was bad news.

I made the junior varsity team.

The range of emotions started to hit me. Shock, disbelief, and anger, which repeated all over again. Shock, disbelief, anger, and then out of nowhere came another emotion—questioning.

I started questioning my abilities. I started questioning my passion. I started questioning the work I had put in. I started questioning the coaches at the soccer camp and why they would give me an MVP award.

I also realized the goal I had set in that hot, sweaty, light blue Ford Taurus that my grandma drove was not met. I had failed.

My ultimate goal of making the varsity team didn't happen.

My dad picked me up from school that day. I didn't say a word. He didn't ask any questions. He must have known what had happened and wanted to give me space.

I went to my room and didn't come down until dinner. My mom called me down, and I pushed the food around my plate. My family had a conversation around me for a while, until finally my sister shouted at me.

"What happened? Something is up, isn't it? Seems like you're mad at the world."

My family was supportive, and I felt like I could talk to them, so I started the story. It did feel good to talk to them about it, but everything I was saying was from a negative point of view.

I mentioned how I had set a goal, and I failed at that goal. Things were coming out of my mouth like, "Maybe I'm not good enough." "I'll probably never make the team." "I should find a new sport or hobby."

My dad cut in. "Stop feeling sorry for yourself. Do you realize all the good that you did this summer to improve your game?" He continued, "You won the MVP for your age group at a large soccer camp. You don't need me to remind you of all the improvement and the good things that came to you. You know all of this. You're just not letting yourself think about them.

"Stop focusing on the negative. You missed your goal. So what? Let me tell you this: I've missed plenty of goals in my life, but you can't always focus on what happens at the end.

"Even if you miss a goal, you still learn from it. You didn't make the varsity team, but did you improve as a player?"

"Yes," I said.

"Then you have two choices to make. You can quit the game and forget about everything that happened and all the work that went into the summer, or you can take this as a challenge and keep your head down, work your butt off on the JV team, and keep the goal alive. Just because you didn't make the team now doesn't mean you're never going to make it."

He said one more thing that really hit me.

"A goal can't be looked at under a microscope and just at the very end. Look at the whole picture and the journey you just took to get to the end. Even if the result isn't what you wanted, don't take it as a complete failure.

"Look at the good and take that. Look at the bad and throw those parts away. Then reset your goal, tie up your shoes, and keep on your journey.

"This is just one small setback for a big comeback. That's the attitude you need to succeed, for this and for your whole life."

It started to make sense. It still sucked, but it would be crazy to let it derail my path. This was a long trip, and honestly, I was a sophomore, and this was such a small stumble.

When you set goals, remember to look back at not only the results, but what happened along the way.

Chances are you won't remember the end, but you'll remember how you felt during the process.

Go back to the hockey goal I outlined above. Do you think when you're 50 you'll remember you only scored nine goals that year? No chance. You'll remember your teammates and the feelings you had during the season.

Whatever journey you're on, try to remember it's more about the path you're traveling and not the result.

It's like going on a roller coaster ride. You just waited in a long line and finally got on the ride. You got buckled in and you think about all the ups and downs and turns you don't expect that are about to come. Many things are going through your mind as you sit there, waiting to take off on the trip. One thing that isn't going through your mind is, "I can't wait until the end of this."

You want to enjoy the *whole* ride and that's why you're here, for the ride. When you do get to the end, you aren't going to judge it based off how it ended. You're going to tell your friends about this turn and how you went upside down at one point. You'll tell them how the overall ride was great.

This is how we should think about our goals and the moments in our life. Even if the result isn't exactly how we pictured it or how we wanted it, we still can learn from it and look at the journey to see the good times in it.

When you pick a goal and work your hardest to hit it but don't, treat yourself how you'd want someone else to treat you. Pick yourself up, take the good that happened, ask yourself what you could have done differently, and get back to work!

Closing

You've made it to the end. I hope these stories were easily digestible and easy to read. I hope you can take pieces back with you as you get back to your life.

These stories, tips, and tricks are not backed by science. They aren't proven. They are merely my opinions. There is no black and white in these chapters, and the questions can't be answered with a simple yes or no.

These are only helpful tips that I think are valuable. You may disagree with some things and agree with others. That's ok. This is meant to give you examples for how to handle thoughts that you may be having. This is not any sort of medical advice and should not be used as such. This is entertainment with lessons baked inside.

If you are struggling with thoughts and problems, do not be afraid to talk to someone. Whoever it is, someone is willing to listen to you, and you should never feel embarrassed to talk about a struggle, because everyone struggles.

That said, this kind of stuff isn't easy. I struggle with these things daily, but guess what, so does everyone else.

A lot of this book comes from a journey I have been on, trying to learn as much as I can about successful people. They may be athletes, musicians, people in business, people in the self-help space, or anyone who I can read about or listen to their story.

All of them have had the same struggle and learning path that we are on. They are no different than you or me.

I've listened to podcasts, read books, and watched videos. I'll continue to follow this pattern, as I'm truly curious about people and their stories—where they came from, how they've "made it," and their outlook on life. The common theme among all these stories is that they were all different.

They all had a different story and a different recipe to success. While I know there is always more than one way to do something, I've been in certain roles in my life that had a cookie cutter process, so I thought maybe there is one way that works for everything.

I read about people who had contrasting backgrounds. I listened to people who worked differently. I read about athletes who worked out at 4 am and people who didn't work out until 4 pm. I watched people talk about working seven days a week, and I read about people who worked 5 hours a week. There were people who had a rigid schedule, and people who kept it laid back and open.

So what did I take away? I learned that if I try to follow someone else's rules, I'm not going to enjoy my own version of success. I need to stay true to myself because no one wants to live like someone else. There isn't just one right way to do something. I learned this at a young age. I also hate feeling like I'm not being exactly myself, like I'm trying to be someone else.

One thing all these successful people had in common was that they were telling their story for a reason. They were all inspiring, but every single one of them had a different beginning and middle. Most were still on their journey and at varying points. There isn't only one process to follow.

Don't take my stories as ways you should live your life. Use them as stories, tips, and tricks that have worked for me. This is just a little guidance.

Do it your way!

My last thought is this: Remember what I said about constantly learning? You also need to constantly work to improve. When I was a kid, I thought there was an end goal. Maybe the goal was a wife, children, a big house, a nice job, being a professional athlete, or having lots of money in the bank, but there is no end goal. You will achieve things you want along the way, but there is no end until you leave this earth. It is about the process of life and not the ending. One of my stories was about "process over outcome," and you should truly listen to what that means. If you enjoy the process while constantly learning and improving, you will get your outcome. When you get to that outcome, you will learn that the process was the only part that really mattered. All the little steps it took for you to get there were the most important part of it all.

I am far from my outcome and so is everyone on this planet, including you. It is a journey of discovery. You will have rough times and you will have smooth times. Enjoy the rough times as much as the smooth and try to see the worth in them. It isn't easy, but if you continue to have an open mind, learn new things, and improve what you can, it will be worth it. Trust me, I am living proof.

"Enjoy when you can and endure when you must."

Made in United States
North Haven, CT
23 March 2022

17458743R00045